BIG WHEELS

by Anne Rockwell

A TRUMPET CLUB SPECIAL EDITION

for Olly

Published by The Trumpet Club
666 Fifth Avenue, New York, New York 10103

Copyright © 1986 by Oliver Penn Rockwell

ISBN 0-440-84623-4

This edition published by arrangement with Dutton
Children's Books, a division of Penguin Books USA Inc.

Editor: Ann Durell   Designer: Isabel Warren-Lynch

Printed in the United States of America
September 1992

1 3 5 7 9 10 8 6 4 2
DAN

Big wheels work for us.

Front loaders lift dirt.

Bulldozers push it.

Clamshell cranes dig deep holes.

Wrecking balls on cranes
knock down old buildings.

Power shovels dig up

big rocks and dirt.

Dump trucks dump gravel.

Cement mixers turn wet cement
around and around.

Tractor scrapers have the biggest wheels of all.

They make new roads.

Big heavy rollers roll a new road smooth.

A sweeper with brushes keeps our streets clean.

Snowplows push and shove

snow off the roads in winter.

A compactor has big sharp wheels

that chop up garbage at the city dump.

The farmer's tractor pulls the plow
that turns the earth over in spring

so seeds can grow.

A combine cuts the wheat

that makes our bread.

Big wheels are good.
They help us every day.